Reading for comprehen[sion]

Contents

Teachers' notes

Introduction

This book contains activity sheets for sequencing and cloze procedure. It is intended for children working at Key Stage 2.

These activities are not designed as teaching tools in themselves, but rather they offer children practice in newly acquired skills. In order that children gain the maximum benefit from these activities, it is essential that they are incorporated into a learning environment which offers time for talking, listening, thinking, telling, reading and writing.

There is always a danger with photocopiable sheets that children will see them simply as time-fillers. Always explain the purpose of the activity so that they concentrate on that aspect of the task.

Aims of this book

• To encourage reading for meaning.
• To help children to see logical connections within texts.
• To focus upon particular parts of speech.
• To assist children in constructing coherent writing.

Sequencing

Sequencing activities present children with sections of text which are not in the correct order which they are then required to reorder into a sensible sequence. Such activities promote logical thinking and encourage children to pay careful attention to the precise meaning of the text in front of them.

These tasks demand a broken, reflective read and the children need to consider each section before completing the organisation of the whole text. This is important as many children who have acquired initial fluency in reading can become over-casual, particularly when reading fiction. They are content to extract just the gist of a story and fail to attend to any more subtle meanings. Tasks which require them to fully comprehend all aspects of the text are an important means by which they can become familiar with the essentials of successful reading – the persistent search for meaning.

Demonstrate a sequencing activity before asking the children to complete a particular task. It is suggested that they undertake the sequencing tasks in pairs, as the resulting discussion about the order of the text often confirms the learning. The children have to justify their choices to one another and this consolidates their knowledge. Discussing together why a certain piece of text cannot follow another, helps them to understand the causal connections in texts. Sometimes children are asked to work in pairs but, in fact, work as two individuals sitting close to one another! Giving each pair only one copy of the sequencing sheet can result in profitable discussion and negotiation of answers.

Page 32 is a blank master sheet for use with some of the sequencing activities. You will need to provide blank paper for the others. The children should cut up each text page as indicated and then stick the strips of text on to the blank sections. Tell the children to position the text in what they believe to be the right order and then to reread the whole text to check for continuity before fixing the text in place.

Cloze procedure

Cloze procedure was originally devised as a means of assessing the readability of a text. It is now widely used as a means of assessing the extent to which a reader has fully comprehended a text.

The text is presented with gaps and the children must read attentively in order to make accurate predictions about which words would fill the gaps. When children complete the deletions, they bring their own language and knowledge to reading the text. Thus, it becomes more meaningful and important to them. Cloze procedure tasks generate a considerable amount of thinking about a text and they also encourage prediction, as the child is required to read ahead to seek justification for the word selected to fill the gap.

The children should be encouraged to read the whole text (or at least the whole sentence) before inserting a missing word. Often a clue to the most accurate word lies in text which follows the gap. This encourages children to see the fluency of writing and the continuity of texts.

Remind the children that cloze deletions do not necessarily have only one correct response. Tell them to jot down in rough all their suggestions and then decide which is the most appropriate, trying to be sensitive to the style of the author. Children usually like to compare their 'answers' with the ones provided and this checking and comparing can become part of the learning process. Discuss why their particular word, although appropriate, might not be as good as the one provided in the answers. Similarly, encourage them to defend their choice of word. All of this negotiation heightens children's awareness of the appropriacy of language.

All children, but particularly hesitant spellers, should be reassured that exciting words are valued and that spelling can always be checked once the most suitable word has been selected.

It can often be valuable to organise the children into pairs of mixed ability. The weaker reader has support for the reading of the text and the more able reader may have to explain their reasons for suggesting any particular word. This 'teaching' is a very effective way of learning.

There are different types of cloze procedure. Some passages have 'random deletions'. This means that words have been deleted in a regular cycle, for example, every ninth word. This kind of cloze is used on pages 11–13, where the activities are graded in difficulty. There are deletions approximately every ninth or tenth word in the easiest activity and every seventh or eighth word for the most difficult. Other cloze activities are based on 'specific deletions'. This means that specific vocabulary has been deleted to encourage the child to reuse particular aspects of language. For example, in a non-fiction text it can be very useful to delete new technical vocabulary as a means of checking whether the child has absorbed its meaning. Specific deletions can also be applied to parts of speech to encourage children to concentrate upon specific tools of language, for example adjectives, verbs or adverbs. The activities in this book offer practice in all kinds of specific deletions.

Point out that the length of the line does not indicate the length of the deleted word.

Children often assume that the word deleted must be an 'important' word and this means that they are not expecting the word to be 'on', 'in' or 'by'. Remind them that these little words also have an important part to play in the cohesive construction of a text.

Notes on individual activities

Pages 5–10: Cloze and sequencing

These activities are arranged in linked pairs. This means, for example, that there is a cloze activity followed by a sequencing activity both on the topic of the Romans. These dual tasks avoid what can otherwise be the isolated nature of such activities. The children can take their interest in one activity forward into the next. Each sequencing activity is only broadly linked with its related cloze activity, but it helps children to appreciate how knowledge is interconnected. The deletions are every ninth or tenth word giving children a range of words to supply. Give the children copies of the blank master sheet (page 32) to fit the sequenced text into whenever appropriate.

Answers

Page 5 sequenced order: 3, 2, 1, 4, 6, 5.
Page 6 missing words: Romans, more, people, in, lines, horse, one, street, the, in, took, meet, was.
Page 7 sequenced order: 3, 2, 1, 6, 4, 5.

Page 8 missing words: burning, window, terrifying, to, other, our, frightened, was, both, and, packed, held.
Page 9 sequenced order: 3, 1, 6, 4, 2, 5.
Page 10 missing words: carried, We, in, train, seat, one, helped, held, We, arm, sprang, soldiers, heard, brother.

Pages 11–13: Cloze – newspaper articles

These cloze activities are presented as newspaper-style articles. When completing a cloze passage it is important that children are sensitive to the style and genre of the passage. Newspaper reports, for example, have a particular journalistic style.

Answers

Page 11 missing words: be, popular, coconut, It, be, will, There, out, excitement, likely, very, Sale, catch, delicious, young.
Page 12 missing words: to, spot, really, match, minute, defence, but, the, missed, It, after, almost, ecstatic, hope.
Page 13 missing words: fast, nesting, are, to, houses, if, came, the, set, barn, other, would, sure, the, supplying, over, place, help.

Pages 14–18: Poetry sequencing

These activities require the children to reorder lines from poems. The first poem does not rhyme. The children will have to follow the humorous logic of the lines to sequence the poem. The first line has been indicated. The subsequent poems are graded in difficulty. It is worth pointing out to the children that the poem 'Robin sang sweetly' can begin with lines about summer or with lines about autumn. Ask the children which they prefer and why. Does the chosen beginning affect the poem? The most challenging activity is 'The thrush's nest'. Advise the children to look carefully at the rhyming pattern. As the rhyming sequence is more complex it is difficult to predict the sequence. It might be more appropriate to give some pairs the starting lines for this poem. Encourage them to learn the poems by heart.

Answers

Page 14 sequenced order: 1, 8, 4, 11, 5, 10, 2, 7, 3, 9, 6.
Page 15 sequenced order: 3, 1, 4, 6, 2, 5.
Page 16 sequenced order: 4, 2, 6, 1, 5, 3.
Page 17 sequenced order: 3, 7, 6, 4, 2, 8, 5, 1.
Page 18 sequenced order: 1, 3, 6, 2, 7, 5, 4.

Pages 19–21: Cloze – story passages

These activities are all based around well-known children's fiction. In the first activity, 'A pony and trap ride' (from *The Secret Garden*), all the deletions are of verbs. In 'Wild cherries' (from *The Railway Children*), all the deletions are of adjectives. In 'Holiday at sea' (from *Swallows and Amazons*), all the deletions are of adverbs. Before the children undertake these activities, it is essential to check that they are familiar with these parts of speech. It is also interesting to note that with these specific deletions there are always more variations of words that fit semantically into the gaps. Encourage the children to make lists of these words before completing the photocopiable page and to decide which word they prefer.

Answers

Page 19 missing words: arrived, was, discover, curled, kept, cast, caught, drove, saw, passed, noticed, began, were, hear.
Page 20 missing words: sunny, beautiful, wild, steep, young, large, white, old, ripe, precious, great, empty.
Page 21 missing words: tidily, gently, slowly, quickly, excitedly, steadily, loudly, eagerly, happily, uncontrollably, wearily.

Pages 22-24: Sequencing – traditional tales

These activities are based around well-known stories ('The musicians of Bremen', 'The elves and the shoemaker', 'The fisherman and his wife') which should help the children with the task of sequencing the text. Since these tales should be familiar to the children, the extracts of text in each section are quite long.

Extension activity

Ask the children to work in pairs to write out a well-known story. Then tell them to cut up the stories into six or seven sections and ask other children to resequence them. The children will initially need help in writing the tale with enough clues as to the next episode. Encourage them to think of the story in separate paragraphs and to write it out with clear spaces between each section as this will make it easier for the children who are to resequence the story.

Answers

Page 22 sequenced order: 3, 1, 6, 4, 2, 5.
Page 23 sequenced order: 5, 3, 2, 6, 1, 4.
Page 24 sequenced order: 4, 1, 5, 3, 6, 2.

Pages 25–27: Information and cloze

These activities are all based around the theme 'Discoveries'. The task is different from the previous cloze passages in which the children are expected to complete the gaps drawing upon their own language knowledge. In these activities, the deletions are content words specific to the topic and so the children are expected to read the passage at the top of the page carefully and then to use the new vocabulary from it to complete the cloze passage in the lower half of the page. This encourages children to read information in a more deliberate and thoughtful way.

Answers

Page 25 missing words: young, Howard Carter, important, four, throne, gold, clothing, Egypt, greatest.

Page 26 missing words: 1982, sea, spectacular, world, sank, VIII, French, successful, preserved.

Page 27 missing words: 1905, spinning, gyroscope, axis, movement, gyroscope, 1908, navigation.

Pages 28-31: Sequencing instructions and directions

These activities give children practice in presenting a set of instructions in the correct order. This is a skill which some children find particularly difficult. They may be aware of the things that need to be done in order to complete a task but they are uncertain about the precise sequence of events. These activities also give children the opportunity to handle the particular ways in which we present instructions using the imperative form of the verb; that is, 'add', 'turn', 'sift' and so on.

Extension activity

Encourage the children to devise their own maps. They should provide a clear set of instructions to help another pair to reach an objective; for example they could draw a treasure map with gold hidden somewhere or a map of the school and give directions to a certain room.

National Curriculum: English

The activities in this book support the following requirements of the PoS for KS2 for the National Curriculum for English:

Speaking and Listening
- Pupils should be given opportunities to talk for a range of purposes, including:
  - exploring, developing, and explaining ideas;
  - sharing ideas, insights and opinions;
- Pupils should be taught to use an increasingly varied vocabulary. The range of pupils' vocabulary should be extended and enriched through activities that focus on words and their meanings.

Reading
- Pupils should be encouraged to develop as enthusiastic, independent and reflective readers. They should be introduced to a wide range of literature, and have opportunities to read extensively for their own interest and pleasure, and for information;
- Pupils should read and use a wide range of sources of information;
- Pupils should be taught to consider in detail the quality and depth of what they read. They should be encouraged to respond imaginatively to the ... vocabulary and organisation of language in literature;
- Pupils should be taught how to find information in books and computer-based sources by using organisational devices to help them decide which parts of the material to read closely. They should be given opportunities to read for different purposes, adopting appropriate strategies for the task, including skimming to gain an overall impression, scanning to locate information and detailed reading to obtain specific information. Pupils should be taught to:
  - identify the precise information that they wish to know;
  - re-present information in different forms;
- They should be encouraged to use their knowledge gained from reading to develop their understanding of the structure, vocabulary and grammar of standard English.

Writing
- Pupils should be given opportunities to write for varied purposes, understanding that writing is essential to thinking and learning;
- They should write in response to a wide range of stimuli;
- They should be taught to use the characteristics of different kinds of writing... The forms in which they write should include ... non-fiction, eg ... instructions;
- They should be encouraged to make judgements about when a particular tone, style, format or choice of vocabulary is appropriate;
- Pupils should be taught to distinguish between words of similar meaning, to explain the meanings of words and to experiment with choices of vocabulary. Their interest in words should be extended by the discussion of language use and choices.

See inside back cover for Scottish 5-14 Curriculum and Northern Ireland Curriculum links

The Roman invasion of Britain

After their defeat in 50 BC, the Britons promised to pay money to Rome and stop supporting the Gauls. Consequently, the Romans sailed away, only to return 100 years later.

Caesar wanted to punish the Britons for supporting the Gauls, so he sailed across the Channel. His army defeated the Britons in a fierce fight on the beach.

In 50 BC the Britons were helping their allies, the Gauls, to fight against the Roman Empire. The Romans were led by a famous general called Julius Caesar.

So a hundred years later, in AD 50, the Romans returned to conquer Britain. They wanted to make it part of the powerful Roman Empire.

Finally, the Britons had to accept defeat. The Romans continued to rule most of Britain for nearly 400 years.

The Britons fought bravely, led by their chief whose name was Caractacus. However, the Roman army was stronger, better trained and well organised.

● Name _____

A Roman town

When the Romans came to Britain there were no real towns or ports, just villages and settlements.

As in all other parts of their empire, the _____ set to work to build towns. It was _____ civilised, easier to collect taxes and enforce laws if _____ lived in towns.

A Roman town was set out _____ an orderly way. The streets crossed each other in straight _____. The main streets were paved and wide enough for a _____ and cart to pass. There were stepping stones connecting _____ pavement to another.

Small shops lined the main _____, but the Roman slaves did most of the shopping in _____ market-place or forum. The forum was a wide, open space _____ the centre of the town. Public meetings _____ place there. Most towns had public baths where people would _____, not only to wash but also to meet friends. There _____ often a theatre for plays and sporting events.

You can still see evidence of the Roman occupation in many towns and cities in Britain today.

The Great Fire of London

The Lord Mayor ordered houses to be pulled down to check the path of the fire. This did not work as the fire overtook their attempts.

At that time, houses were built very close together and many of the houses were made of wood. They burned easily and helped the fire to spread quickly.

The Great Fire of London started in a baker's shop in Pudding Lane. The year was 1666. The fire quickly spread through the city, destroying many churches including St Paul's Cathedral.

Finally, groups of sailors blew up houses with gunpowder which was much quicker. The wider gaps eventually stopped the spread of the fire.

London was rebuilt within six years. Houses were built of brick and stone and streets were wider and cleaner. Sir Christopher Wren rebuilt St Paul's Cathedral which can be seen today.

When the houses were pulled down, the terrified people fled to the River Thames with what belongings they could salvage. They jumped into boats hoping to cross the river to safety.

Fleeing to safety – an extract from a child's diary

We had gone to bed early that particular day. My mother and father had guests and were dining late.

I woke suddenly. I was aware of a strong smell of _____.

I rushed out of bed and looked out of the high casement _____.

A scene of great confusion met my eyes.

Most _____ of all was a long line of flames that seemed

_____ stretch from one end of London to the _____.

It lit up the sky and was advancing towards _____ house. Both

the cracking of the flaming timbers and the _____ shouts of the

people in the streets below added to the chaos.

My father, who _____ white and shaken, woke my sister and

hurried us _____ downstairs. My mother tied damp cloths over

our mouths _____ took us out to a cart which was already

_____ with our belongings.

When we were finally in the boat, crossing the Thames to safety, I looked

back. I _____ my sister's hand and smiled at my exhausted

parents. At least my family were safe. September 2nd 1666, I knew, was a

night I would never forget.

A wartime memory

I had to make sure that my brother was awake. He used to be very bad-tempered if he was disturbed in the night and he wanted to go back to sleep.

The Anderson shelter was dug into the ground. It had no heating and it always felt cold. My brother always used to grab the top bunk. There was often a puddle of rainwater on the rough cement floor.

If we heard the air-raid siren in the night we had to get up and put on warm clothes over our night things. We had to wear our shoes because it was often wet as we walked down the garden.

Mum used to hurry us down the garden path to the Anderson shelter. We weren't allowed to use the light so we often bumped into things. My dad was not with us. He was a soldier and we didn't even know where he was.

We could hear the planes going overhead and the thud of guns, but mum used to tell us not to worry. We would fall asleep and stay in the Anderson shelter until morning.

The twins, who were only babies, had to be put in the wicker laundry basket. They didn't even wake up. They had a stone hot-water bottle, wrapped in a blanket, to help keep them warm.

A wartime journey

It was cold. The station was crowded. It was bustling with soldiers with kitbags, wailing children, engines steaming gently and noise everywhere.

Everyone _____ a gas mask case. I was lucky that I was with

my mum and my brothers. _____ were leaving London to stay

with an aunt _____ a safe part of the country.

The _____ was in the station and everyone surged forward

to try and get a _____ on the train. My mum had my baby

brother in _____ arm and a large suitcase in the other. A

soldier took the suitcase and _____ her to a seat in the

carriage. I carried the baby's food and our sandwiches and _____

tightly to my mum's coat.

The train was full. _____ heard the whistle blow. My mother

clutched my _____. Where was John? My heart missed a beat. I

_____ up and pushed my way into the corridor shouting 'John!

John!' I couldn't get past the _____. I was crying now.

Suddenly I _____ an embarrassed shout, 'I'm here!' It was my

_____, he was on the train. I went back into the carriage and

smiled at my mum through my tears. It was all right, we were still all

together.

Morley Fun Day

On Saturday 9 August, from midday until late, there will be a Fun Day in Morley. It will be held on the playing field of Richard Morley Primary School.

There will _____ lots of activities taking place including the

immensely _____ 'Welly throwing'. You can try your luck at the

_____ shy or maybe have a go at skittles. _____

looks easy, doesn't it?

    The highlight, of course, will _____ the incredible spectacle

of ferret racing, and there _____ be an opportunity to bet on

the winner. _____ will be local school teams battling it

_____ in five-a-side football which always brings _____

to the supporters. Young visitors are more _____ to get excited

about the bouncy castle – a _____ popular feature.

    Take a look at the Car Boot _____, there is a chance of a

bargain here! Use the Fun Day to see your friends, _____ up

on the gossip and perhaps try one of Mrs Reid's _____ cakes

as well.

    Morley Fun Day promises to be a great day out for _____

and old alike. Don't forget, 9 August, BE THERE!

Football report

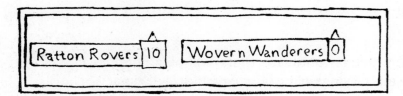

What a match! What a disaster! With last season's top scorer failing a late fitness test, Wovern Wanderers could only field a team of ten.

The first corner of the game went _____ Wanderers, but it was the

only high _____. They lost their way in spite of working

_____ hard to compensate for the missing striker. The miss of the

_____ came in the tenth _____ when Towner raced

clear of Rover's _____. Smith raced out to try and intercept,

_____ Towner rounded him with ease. He approached

_____ net with not another player near, took aim and

_____! The groans echoed around the Wovern football ground.

_____ was downhill from then on. Goal _____ goal

until the tenth was received in _____ total silence by the Wovern

supporters and _____ joy by visiting Rovers.

The Wanderers must _____ for a quick recovery by Ken

Watchen. Next week can only be better!

● Name _____

The Hoot and Screech Club

READ THIS, IT'S IMPORTANT!

Hi! I'm Harold Hoot. Did you know that owls in Britain are having a hard time of it?

Their traditional nesting sites are disappearing _____. Woodland

is being chopped down so _____ in hollow trees becomes tricky.

Barns _____ being converted into houses or razed

_____ the ground to make way for _____

and roads. How would you feel _____ you were an owl and when

it _____ to nesting-time and you fancied _____

same home as last year, you _____ off, and when you arrived the

_____ had gone and there were no _____ suitable

homes for miles around? It _____ put you right off laying, I'm

_____ .

  So, how can you help? Well _____ Hoot and Screech

Club are _____ nesting boxes for suitable sites all

_____ Britain. If you know of a _____ where

an owl could nest, or want to _____ in any way get in touch with

this club. The address is on the back page of the paper.

  Remember – an owl in a nest,
      an owl has a rest.

Why are fire engines red?

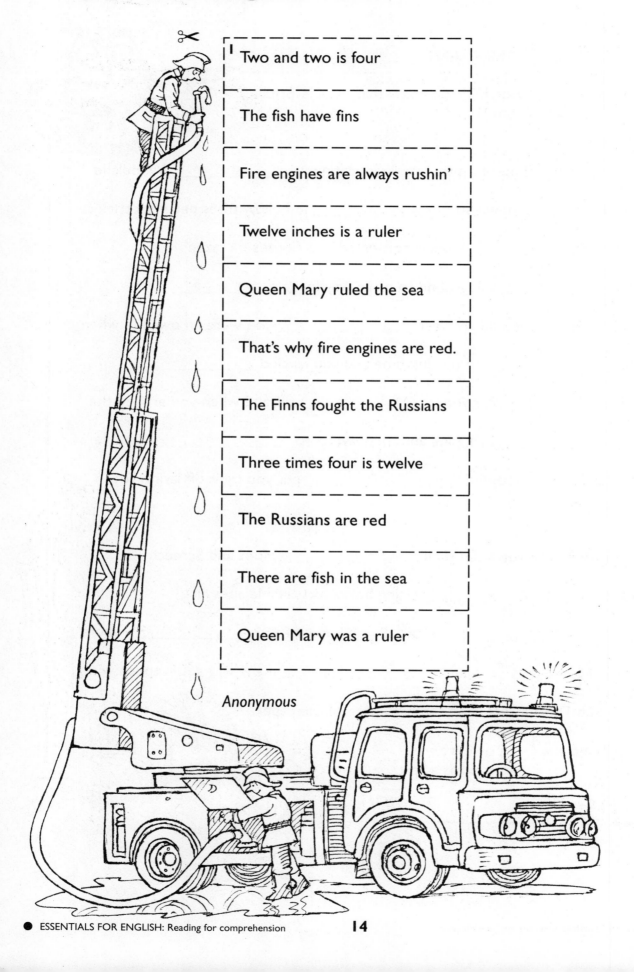

Two and two is four

The fish have fins

Fire engines are always rushin'

Twelve inches is a ruler

Queen Mary ruled the sea

That's why fire engines are red.

The Finns fought the Russians

Three times four is twelve

The Russians are red

There are fish in the sea

Queen Mary was a ruler

Anonymous

King Arthur

He stole three sacks of barley meal
To make a bag-pudding.

The king and queen sat down to dine,
And all the court beside;

When good King Arthur ruled the land,
He was a goodly king;

A bag-pudding the queen did bake,
And stuffed it full of plums,

And what they could not eat that night,
The queen next morning fried.

And in it put great lumps of fat,
As big as my two thumbs.

Anonymous

It's school today

I wave to Mum and shut the gate
I'll have to hurry it's half-past eight.

I wash my face, I brush my hair,
I hang my nightdress on the chair.

I reach the gate: it's five to nine.
Goodness me! I'm just in time.

I wake up early, it's school today,
I'll get up early and be on my way.

The bus has gone, I'll run to school.
I pass the shops and the swimming pool.

The breakfast table is all set,
I'll eat it quickly and feed my pet.

Anonymous

Robin sang sweetly

✂

When the spring came back again,
He sang, 'I told you so!'

In the cold and wintry weather
Still you hear his song.

Robin sang sweetly
When the days were bright.

'There are fruits for everyone.
Let us all give praise!'

Keep on singing through the winter;
'It will always go.'

Robin sang sweetly
In the autumn days:

'Thanks! Thanks for summer!'
He sang with all his might.

'Somebody must sing,' said Robin,
'Or winter will seem long.'

Anonymous

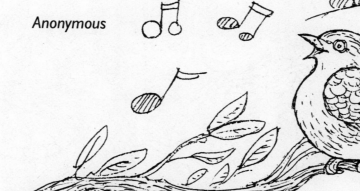

The thrush's nest

(This poem, by John Clare, was written over a hundred years ago.)

Within a thick and spreading hawthorn bush
That overhung a molehill large and round,

How true she warped the moss to form a nest,
And modelled it with in the wood and clay;

I heard from morn to morn a merry thrush
Sing hymns to sunrise, and I drank the sound.

A brood of nature's minstrels chirp and fly
Glad as that sunshine and the laughing sky.

Ink spotted over shells of greeny blue;
And there I witnessed, in the sunny hours,

With joy; and, often an intruding guest,
I watched her secret toils from day to day –

And by and by, like heath bells gilt with dew,
There lay her shining eggs, as bright as flowers,

A pony and trap ride

Mary is going on holiday to stay with an aunt and uncle whom she has never met. They live on the edge of a wild moor.

It was late at night when Mary _____ at the station and the

wind was howling. She _____ surprised to _____

that the remainder of her journey was by pony and trap.

Mary _____ up in the corner of the trap and

_____ her eyes on the road ahead. The lamps on the trap

_____ rays of light a little distance ahead. Mary

_____ fleeting glimpses of the things they passed.

They _____ through a tiny village and she

_____ whitewashed cottages and the lights of a public house.

They _____ an ancient church and a large vicarage. She

_____ the lights of a shop window. Then the village was gone.

At last the trotting horses _____ to go more slowly, as if

they _____ climbing a steep hill. She could see nothing now but

a wall of darkness on either side of the trap. She could _____

the panting of the horses. She leaned forward, the trap gave an enormous

jolt and lurched to a stop. They were there.

● Name _____

Wild cherries

A long time ago three children lived in a small cottage in the country. They were very poor and were searching for a present for their mother who was recovering from an illness.

Wild cherries! This idea occurred to the children when they woke up

that _____ morning. They had seen the _____

blossom on the trees in the spring and knew where to look for

_____ cherries now that cherry-time was here.

Many trees grew along the _____ bank of the river which

the _____ children were not allowed to climb.

There were all sorts of trees growing there. Birches and beeches and

_____ oaks and hazels and among them the _____

blossom shone like snow.

Mother had let them take their lunch in an _____ basket. It

would do to carry the _____ cherries back in; if they found

any. Mother also lent them her _____ silver watch so that they

would not be late for tea.

With _____ care the children picked the cherries. They all

tried to reach the cherries at the ends of the branches. Soon they had filled

the _____ basket and they carried it triumphantly home.

Holiday at sea

John and Wendy climbed down the steps into the noisy and bustling harbour. The sun shone brightly and there wasn't a cloud in the sky.

This was the first day of their first ever sailing holiday. They grinned at each other. They were excited. The luggage had to be stowed _____ in the cabin because there wasn't much room. It wasn't a very big boat. The wind was blowing _____ and they could feel the boat moving _____ against the harbour wall.

The children had been told they could go down to the beach for a swim. They _____ put on their swimming costumes, left the boat and ran _____ to the nearby beach.

John looked at the waves, rolling _____ down the beach. He shouted _____ to Wendy and jumped _____ into the waves. They were so strong that he struggled to keep his balance. Then Wendy ran into the sea and, holding John's hand, they jumped _____ in the waves.

Eventually the sun went in. John began to shiver _____ and they both grabbed their towels. They clambered _____ back to the boat.

Dinner was ready. Tomorrow they would set sail. Then, the holiday would really begin!

The travelling musicians

They came across a house in which a band of robbers were feasting, so the animals practised their music. The ass brayed loudly, the dog barked fiercely, the cat meowed shrilly and the cock crowed hoarsely.

The robber thought a witch with long bony fingers had scratched his face, a man with a knife had stabbed him in the leg, a monster had hit him with a club and a devil was shouting at him from above.

An old ass, a dog, a cat and a cockerel, no longer wanted by their owners, decided to set off to the city to become musicians.

When all was dark, one brave robber came back. However, the cat scratched and spat at him and the dog bit him in the leg. The ass kicked him and the cockerel crowed loudly from the top of the house.

Having told his friends the frightful story of his ordeal, the robbers never dared go back to the house. So the 'musicians' lived there in peace and harmony for the rest of their lives.

The robbers fled and the animals settled down for the night. The ass slept in the yard and the dog behind the door. The cat curled up by the fire and the cockerel settled on a beam.

The elves and the shoemaker

At midnight, two little elves came and sat on the shoemaker's bench stitching and tapping away. They stayed there until the job of making the shoes was finished. Then they vanished.

Again he cut out the leather in the evening and again he went to bed. In the morning, there were two pairs of beautiful shoes ready to sell, and he continued to find the shoes made up every morning. Soon the shoemaker and his wife became prosperous because many people wanted to buy the beautiful shoes.

The shoemaker cut the leather for the last pair of shoes and then he went to bed. The next morning, to his great surprise, he found the shoes made up and ready to sell. They were beautiful and he sold them quickly. Then he had enough money to buy leather for another two pairs of shoes.

The shoemaker and his wife decided to make the elves some clothes to keep them warm. They set the little clothes out on the bench one night instead of the leather. The elves put them on and danced away, full of delight. They never returned, but the shoemaker continued to prosper.

Once upon a time there lived an honest shoemaker. Both he and his wife always worked very hard, but there came the day when they only had enough leather left for one pair of shoes.

One winter evening, the shoemaker and his wife decided to hide behind a curtain to see if they could solve the mystery of who was helping them by making the shoes.

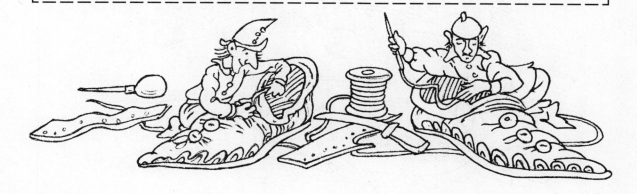

The fisherman and his wife

✂

He hurried home to tell his wife. At once she demanded a pretty little cottage with roses round the door. Her request was granted and she was pleased.

When the fish heard her request he knew that the fisherman's wife would never be content. He turned the stone castle back into a tiny hut again and there she had to live for evermore.

Soon, however, she became dissatisfied with the house. She sent her husband to ask the fish for a stone castle. The fish granted this request and she felt very grand. For a while she was pleased.

A fisherman and his wife lived in a tiny hut by the sea. One day the fisherman caught a large fish. The fish, to his surprise, spoke saying he was an enchanted prince. The fish said he would grant favours if the fisherman would release him. So the fisherman let the fish go.

However, very soon she became dissatisfied. The cottage was not large enough and she wanted a house with a garden. The fish answered the request once more and for a while she was pleased.

Eventually, the stone castle was not enough, so the fisherman had to ask the fish to change the castle for a sparkling palace with servants. She would be the queen.

Tutankhamun, the boy-king

● Read this passage very carefully.

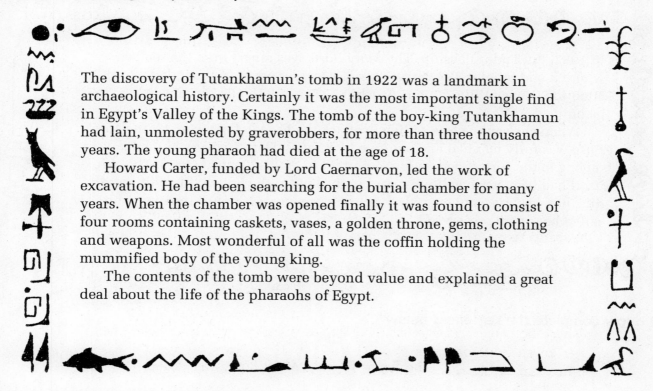

The discovery of Tutankhamun's tomb in 1922 was a landmark in archaeological history. Certainly it was the most important single find in Egypt's Valley of the Kings. The tomb of the boy-king Tutankhamun had lain, unmolested by graverobbers, for more than three thousand years. The young pharaoh had died at the age of 18.

Howard Carter, funded by Lord Caernarvon, led the work of excavation. He had been searching for the burial chamber for many years. When the chamber was opened finally it was found to consist of four rooms containing caskets, vases, a golden throne, gems, clothing and weapons. Most wonderful of all was the coffin holding the mummified body of the young king.

The contents of the tomb were beyond value and explained a great deal about the life of the pharaohs of Egypt.

● Now complete the sentences below.

The tomb of the _____ pharaoh, Tutankhamun, was

discovered by _____ _____ in 1922. It

was an amazing and _____ discovery, for the tomb and

its treasures had remained intact. In the _____ rooms

of the burial chamber there were caskets, vases and a_____

made from _____.

There was also some furniture, _____ and weapons,

showing what life was like in _____ over three

thousand years ago. However, the _____ discovery of

all was the golden splendour of Tutankhamun, the boy-king himself.

● Name _____

The *Mary Rose*

● Read this passage very carefully.

In 1982, the Tudor flagship, The *Mary Rose*, was raised from the sea-bed, where it had lain for 437 years. This spectacular event commanded world attention. Henry VIII's famous flagship was one of the first true warships to be built.

When she sank, while sailing to attack the French fleet in 1545, the *Mary Rose* was fully manned and equipped for battle. Her discovery and her raising to the surface were very important in archaeological terms. The ship itself had been very well preserved in the silts of the Solent. In addition to this, her weapons and everyday tools and the possessions of the men who sailed her, were preserved.

● Now complete the sentences below.

In _____ the Tudor flagship, *Mary Rose*, was raised

from the depths of the _____ near Portsmouth harbour on

the south coast of England. It had been a complicated and

_____ operation and was followed with great interest by

people all over the _____.

The *Mary Rose* _____ in 1545 in front of King Henry

_____ and his court who were watching as the ship sailed

out to meet the _____ fleet. Seven hundred men drowned

and only a few survived.

In the past there had been several attempts at salvaging the ship, but

none had been _____. At an exhibition in Portsmouth are

some 2,000 of the treasures that were _____ in the *Mary*

Rose.

Spinning-tops and the gyroscope

● Read this passage very carefully.

Aeroplanes fly all over the world on automatic pilot. Ships sail across oceans maintaining an even keel in rough seas. Submarines find their way round the ocean depths.

These amazing feats are the result of Elmer Ambrose Sperry's ideas. He was an American. He was watching his child play with a spinning-top in the summer of 1905. The child asked him why it stood up when it spun. It reminded him of a gyroscope, which was used in schools to demonstrate the Earth rotating on its axis.

From this principle, Sperry developed the use of the gyroscope, which keeps pointing the way it is set even when the ship is rolling and pitching. This means that the captain can keep the ship on a level and stable course. In 1908, he developed the gyrocompass which revolutionised navigation in the air and under the water.

● Now complete the sentences below.

Inventions and discoveries often come from small beginnings. In

_____ Elmer Ambrose Sperry was watching his child play

with a _____ top. At this time, in schools, a

_____ was used to show how the Earth turned around

on its _____. The spinning-top reminded him of this

model. As a result of these observations, Sperry was able to design an

instrument which is unaffected by the _____ of the ship.

It was based on the _____. In _____ Sperry

went on to produce the gyrocompass. This allowed precise

_____ in the air and under the water.

Quick pizza

Add the topping that you fancy, such as tomato and cheese, and bake for 25 minutes in a hot oven.

Add 300ml milk to the breadcrumb mixture and mix to a soft dough.

Turn the dough out and knead until smooth.

Sift 450g self-raising flour and 1tsp salt into a bowl.

Roll out the dough and cut into the shape you need.

Rub 100g margarine into the flour and salt until it resembles fine breadcrumbs.

● Write out the recipe in the correct order.

1

2

3

4

5

6

Around town

● Complete this map by reading the sequence of directions below.
● Put arrows along the route you would take.

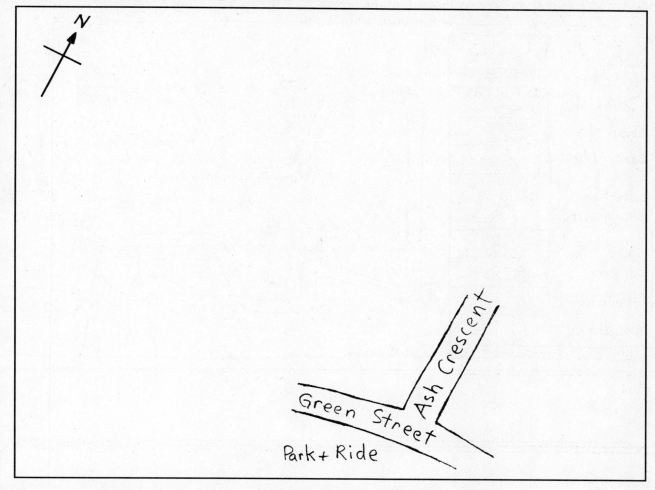

1   From the Park and Ride, catch a bus that goes west along Green
    Street past some trees on the left.

2   Turn right into New Street and get off at the bus stop on the left-
    hand side, opposite a garage.

3   Just past the garage turn right into Church Way, walking past a
    church with a spire on your left.

4   At the end of Church Way, turn left into Ash Crescent to go to the
    chemist's shop on your left.

5   Cross the road by a pedestrian crossing to a baker's shop on the
    opposite side of the road.

6   Follow Ash Crescent round to the south where the road joins
    Green Street opposite the Park and Ride.

Around a country park

● Look at the map below.
● Imagine that you are going to meet a friend at the Museum of Folk Art. Write the directions in sequential order.

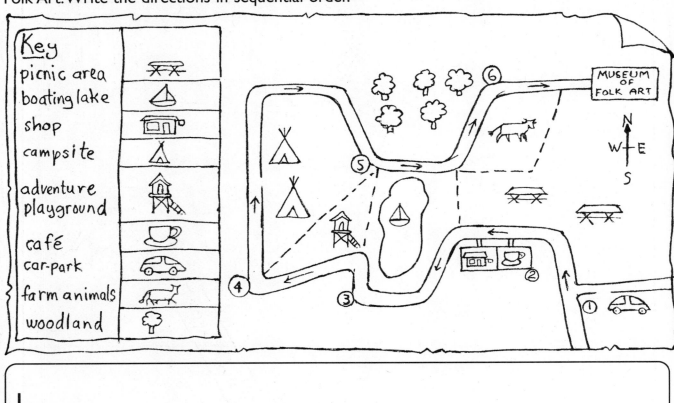

1	

2	

3	

4	

5	

6	

A dog-handling competition

● Look at the diagram below.
● Write instructions for the dog handlers to follow to complete
the course.

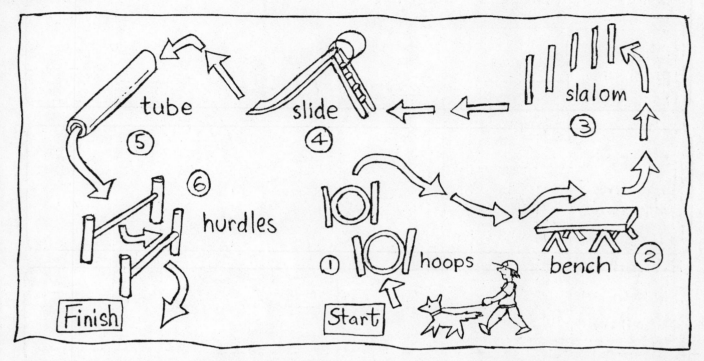

1	
2	
3	
4	
5	
6	

● Name _____

Master sheet for sequencing activities on pages 5, 7, 9, 14, 15, 16, 17, 18, 22, 23 and 24